Positive *Cooking*

Members Favourite
Asian & Oriental
Recipes

Contents

Starters & Side Dishes

Fusion **Fish**

Meat with Mystery

Poultry Paradise

Veritable **Veggies**

We British have fallen in love with the East - especially when it comes to food! But weight loss doesn't have to take a back seat in order to indulge our passion. This collection of members' favourite "Asian & Oriental" recipes proves the point.

Some are your favourites from past Eating Plans which you have asked us to revive, and some are new recipes which we have no doubt will become firm favourites of the future.

All recipes have been counted to fit into the Positive Eating Plan. You'll find calories, Checks and fat gram values for all recipes - minus "free" foods, of course! Most recipes also include "serving suggestions", and we give separate counts when these are added to the recipe. We also tell you what type of meal it is, for those of you who prefer to "Choose Meals" rather than "Choose Checks".

Do check out the "Free Foods" list and "Asian & Oriental" Check List so you can include even more variety and add those essential personal touches.

Enjoy - we're sure you will!

• Calories ◖ Checks ● Fat Grams

Free Foods

Herbs and spices may be used freely on the Positive Eating Plan, as long as they don't have added oil.

Small quantities of seasonings such as soy sauce, beef or yeast extract, stock cubes and a light spray of oil are also "free".

Whenever "free" salad or vegetables are mentioned, you may choose from the following:

Alfalfa sprouts	French beans (greenbeans)
Artichoke hearts	Jerusalem artichokes
Asparagus	Kale
Aubergine	Leeks
Baby sweetcorn	Lettuce, all types
Bamboo shoots	Mangetout/snow peas
Beansprouts	Marrow
Beetroot	Mooli
Bok choi/pak choi	Mushrooms
Broccoli	Okra
Brussels sprouts	Onions, all types
Cabbage, all types	Peppers, all colours
Calabrese	Pumpkin
Carrots	Radishes
Cauliflower	Runner beans
Celeriac	Salsify
Celery	Sauerkraut
Chard	Spinach
Chicory	Spring greens
Chinese leaves	Squash, all types
Christophene (cho-cho)	Sugar snap peas
Courgettes	Swede
Cress	Tomatoes
Cucumber	Turnips
Endive	Water chestnuts
Fennel	Watercress

Remember - "free" foods do not need to be counted on the Positive Eating Plan!

60g mini naan	200	8	7
140g large naan	450	18	16
40g chapatti	120	5	3
1 fried poppadum	75	3	6
1 ready-to-eat or microwaved poppadum	45	2	3
25g prawn crackers	140	6	10
62.5g portion Sharwood's Egg Noodles, boiled	210	8	1
30g dry weight/75g boiled weight basmati rice	100	4	0.5
1 mini onion bhaji	70	3	4
1 mini vegetable pakora	50	2	3
60g meat samosa	175	7	8
60g vegetable samosa	150	6	7
1 medium banana	100	4	0
1 medium mango	100	4	0
1 ring pineapple	20	1	0
3 fresh lychees or rambutans	20	2	0
150g pot low-fat natural yoghurt	90	4	1.5
25g paneer soft Indian cheese	80	3	6
1 tbsp peanut/groundnut oil	120	5	13
1 tsp sesame oil	40	1.5	4
10ml level dspn dessicated coconut	30	1	3
100ml canned coconut milk	160	6	16
100ml reduced fat coconut milk	100	4	10
Sushi ginger		free food	
Curry powder		free food	
15ml tbsp Patak's tandoori curry paste	20	1	0.5
15ml tbsp Patak's balti, rogan josh or tikka masla curry paste	55	2	5
15ml tbsp Patak's korma or madras	80	3	8
Soy sauce or Thai fish sauce		free food	
1 rounded tsp mango chutney	30	1	0
1 rounded tsp lime pickle	30	1	2

nb: values are typical averages across brands and types

Thai Hot Soup

Serves 4

per serving   110

1 tbsp oil
1 bunch spring onions, sliced
4 dried birds eye chillies (e.g. Schwartz)
1 tsp ground ginger
1.1 litres/2 pints chicken stock
1 tbsp lemon juice
60g/2 oz rice noodles (e.g. Sharwoods)
12 tiger prawns
2 tsp dried coriander leaf (e.g. Schwartz)

Heat oil in a large saucepan and fry the spring onions, chillies and ginger for 1-2 minutes.

Add the stock and lemon juice to the pan. Bring to the boil stirring. Add the noodles and prawns and cook 3-4 minutes. Stir in the coriander leaf.

Serve each person with one-quarter of the soup.

Chicken & Sweetcorn Soup

Serves 2

per serving 190

200g can sweetcorn
275ml/½ pint water
1 chicken stock cube
1 tsp soy sauce
150ml/¼ pint skimmed milk
2 spring onions, sliced
1 level dspn cornflour
60g/2 oz cooked chicken, finely chopped

Reserve 2 rounded tbsp of the sweetcorn and liquidise the remainder until creamy, using some of the water if necessary.

Transfer to a saucepan together with the remaining water, crumbled stock cube, soy sauce, skimmed milk and spring onions. Bring to the boil, then simmer 10 minutes.

Mix the cornflour to a smooth paste with a little water and stir into the soup together with the chopped chicken and reserved sweetcorn. Cook 2-3 minutes, stirring continuously.

Serving suggestion

Serve each person with half the soup accompanied by 1 medium slice bread.

per serving 270

or 1 Quick Meal

Szechuan Vegetables

Serves 4

per serving   50   2 2

1 dspn oil
115g/4 oz baby corn cobs
1 small red pepper, de-seeded and cut into strips
60g/2 oz mangetout
3 spring onions, cut into 5cm/2 inch lengths
3 tbsp vegetable stock or water
175g/6 oz button mushrooms, halved
2 cm/1 inch fresh ginger, peeled and grated
2 tbsp light soy sauce
1 dspn clear honey
1 dspn tomato ketchup
2 dspn hot chilli sauce
150g/5 oz fresh beansprouts
1 rounded tsp cornflour

Heat oil in a wok or large frying pan and stir-fry the baby corn, peppers, mangetout and spring onions 3 minutes, adding some stock or water if required.

Add mushrooms and ginger and stir-fry 2 minutes, continuing to add stock or water, a little at a time.

Stir in soy sauce, honey, ketchup and chilli sauce and any remaining stock or water. Add beansprouts and stir-fry 1-2 minutes.

Mix cornflour with a little cold water, add to the pan and cook, stirring until the sauce thickens.

Spicy Prawn Samosas

Makes 18

per samosa   50 **2** (0.5)

225g/8 oz cooked peeled prawns, fresh or frozen, defrosted
115g/4 oz mashed potato
2 dspn curry paste (e.g. Patak's Tikka Curry Paste)
2 dspn chopped coriander or parsley
3 x 45g sheets filo pastry (e.g. Jus-rol)
1 tbsp oil

Mix together the prawns, mashed potato, curry paste and herbs in a bowl. Cover and leave 4 hours or overnight.

Pre-heat oven to 200°C/gas mark 6.

Lay out a sheet of clingfilm slightly larger than the filo sheets and lay the 3 sheets on top. Cut into 6, 1 cut lengthways and 3 crossways, so you now have 18 strips of filo in 3 layers of 6.

Take out 3 strips and cover the rest with clingfilm, so they do not dry out.

Brush each lightly with oil and put 1 dspn of the filling mixture at the bottom of each strip. Fold up in triangles, or make into parcels, sealing the edges with water. Brush lightly with oil and place on a non-stick baking tray.

Repeat until all the pastry and filling are used up and bake for 10-15 minutes until golden brown.

Banana Salad

Serves 4

per serving   60   **2.5** ①

2 medium bananas
Lemon juice
1 green pepper, de-seeded and chopped
2 tomatoes, chopped
5cm/2 inches cucumber, chopped
1 tbsp dessicated coconut
1 tsp curry powder

Peel and slice the bananas and toss in lemon juice to prevent discoloration.

Add remaining ingredients and toss well together, adding more lemon juice to taste.

Serve one-quarter to each person as a side dish with curries.

Raita

total quantity   90 2

150g pot low-fat natural yoghurt
4cm/1½ inches cucumber, grated
Salt
1 tbsp chopped mint or 1 tsp mint sauce
½ tsp granulated sweetener, or to taste (optional)

Mix together the yoghurt and cucumber. Season to taste.

Stir in mint or mint sauce. Taste and add granulated sweetener
if you prefer it less sharp.

Tomato & onion sambal   free food

1 shallot
2-3 tomatoes
Salt and pepper
Lemon or lime juice
1 tsp finely chopped coriander

Peel and chop shallot finely.

Put tomatoes into boiling water for a few seconds. Remove and
peel. Scoop out seeds and chop flesh retaining juices. Mix with
chopped shallot.

Season to taste with salt, pepper and lemon or lime juice and
sprinkle with coriander.

Oriental Salmon

per serving   335   **13**   19

1 tbsp oil
4 x 150g/5 oz salmon fillets
1 bunch spring onions, sliced
2 tsp grated ginger or Schwartz Easy Chopped Ginger
150ml/¼ pint water
3 tbsp dark soy sauce
2 tbsp cornflour
1 tsp runny honey
1 tsp sugar

Heat the oil in a large frying pan and fry the salmon with the spring onions for 3-4 minutes. Turn the salmon, add the ginger and fry for a further minute.

Blend the remaining ingredients together and add to the pan. Bring to the boil, reduce heat and simmer gently 1-2 minutes, stirring occasionally until thickened and glossy and the salmon is cooked through.

Serving suggestion

Boil 125g/half of 250g pack Chinese egg noodles. Serve each person with one salmon fillet, one-quarter of the sauce, one-quarter of the noodles and "free" vegetables stir-fried in spray oil.

per serving   435   **17**   20

or 1 Main Meal plus 1 Check

Indonesian Spiced Rice

Serves 1

per serving   360 **14** 10

or 1 Booster Main Meal

1 small onion, chopped
Spray oil
1 clove garlic, peeled and crushed
2-3 mushrooms, sliced
½ red or green pepper, sliced
1 dspn curry powder, or to taste
1 Oxo chicken cube
2 dspn tomato purée
60g/2 oz rice
275ml/ ½ pint boiling water
30g/1 oz diced ham
60g/2 oz cooked prawns
1 egg, beaten

Sauté the onion in pan sprayed with oil until golden. Add the garlic and cook 1-2 minutes more. Stir in the mushrooms, peppers, curry powder, Oxo cube, tomato purée, rice and boiling water. Cover and cook gently approximately 15-20 minutes, or until rice has absorbed water.

Stir in the ham and prawns and cover to keep warm.

Spray a small pan with oil. Pour in the egg, gradually drawing in the cooked edges, to make an omelette. Remove from pan and cut into thin strips.

Serve the rice mixture topped with omelette strips.

Thai Fish Curry

Serves 1

per serving   200   **8** 7

1 stalk lemon grass
1cm/½ in cube ginger
3-4 slices green chilli, or to taste
2 spring onions, sliced
150ml/¼ pint water
60ml/4 tbsp reduced-fat coconut milk
150g/5 oz cod fillet, or other white fish
1 tsp turmeric
1 dspn Thai fish sauce or light soy sauce
1 tsp cornflour (optional)

Crush the lemon grass stalk with your fist and place in a pan together with the ginger, chilli, spring onions, water and coconut milk. Simmer 10 minutes to infuse the flavours.

Cut the fish into cubes and add to the pan together with the turmeric and Thai fish sauce or soy sauce. Simmer 10 minutes more.

For a thicker sauce, mix the cornflour with a little water and add to pan, stirring until thickened.

Remove the lemon grass stalk and ginger cube before serving.

Serving suggestion

Boil 60g/2 oz rice with your favourite chopped "free" vegetables and serve with fish curry.

per serving   400   **16** 8

or 1 Main Meal

Chinese Trout

Serves 1

per serving   200   8 (8)

150g/5 oz trout
Spray oil
2 spring onions, sliced
2 tsp grated ginger
1 clove garlic, crushed
60g/2 oz mangetout
60g/2 oz baby corn cobs
½ tsp light soy sauce
Juice of ½ lime

Cut trout into 2.5 cm/1 inch chunks.

Spray pan or wok with oil. Add spring onions, ginger, garlic and trout and stir-fry 2-3 minutes.

Add mange tout and corn cobs and cook a further 3-4 minutes or until trout is cooked. Stir in soy sauce and lime juice.

Serving suggestion

Boil 60g/2 oz Chinese egg noodles and serve with trout and vegetables.

per serving   400   16 (9)

or 1 Main Meal

Teriyaki Tuna

Serves 1

per serving   200   **8**   5

100g/3½ oz fresh tuna steak
Spray oil
2 tbsp dry sherry
1 dspn dark soy sauce
2 tsp sugar

Spray pan with oil, heat and cook tuna 2-3 minutes per side, depending on thickness and your personal taste. Do not over-cook. Remove and keep warm.

Add sherry, soy and sugar to pan and stir over medium heat to dissolve sugar. Boil a few seconds to reduce and make "syrupy". Return tuna to pan and heat through gently, coating with the sauce.

Serve sauce poured over tuna.

Serving suggestion

Boil 60g/2 oz rice and serve with Teriyaki Tuna accompanied by "free" salad.

per serving   400   **16**   6

or 1 Main Meal

Seafood Curry

Serves 2

per serving   250

Spray oil
1 small onion, chopped
1 small red pepper, de-seeded and sliced
1 stick celery, finely sliced
1 tbsp curry paste
1 apple, peeled and chopped
1 tbsp raisins
Few drops Worcester sauce
1 tbsp tomato purée
275ml/½ pint water
225g/8 oz haddock or other white fish, cut large chunks
Salt and pepper
85g/3 oz prawns
3 tbsp low-fat natural yoghurt
Squeeze of lemon

Spray a medium saucepan with oil. Add onions, peppers and celery. Cover and cook gently 5 minutes, stirring now and again.

Add curry paste and stir about 30 seconds. Add apple, raisins, Worcester sauce, tomato purée, water and haddock. Stir well and bring to a simmer. Simmer gently 10-15 minutes, stirring now and again.

Add prawns. If using cooked prawns, heat through approximately 1 minute. If using raw prawns cook a few minutes more until they turn pink . Remove from heat and stir in yoghurt and lemon juice just before serving.

Serving suggestion

Boil 85g/3 oz rice and serve each person with half the rice and half the curry.

per serving   400

or 1 Main Meal

Sweet Plum Pork with Fire Cracker Rice

Serves 2

per serving   400 **16** 6

or 1 Main Meal

Recipe used with kind permission of British Meat

200g/7 oz lean, trimmed pork steaks
2 cloves garlic, crushed
Spray oil
2 tomatoes, diced
3 tbsp plum sauce
1 tbsp tomato ketchup
85g/3 oz dry weight rice, boiled
1 red pepper, de-seeded and diced
4 rounded tbsp sweetcorn
2 spring onions, sliced
1 dspn lemon juice
1 tbsp sweet chilli sauce

Cut the pork steaks into thin strips. Spray a large pan or wok with oil and heat. Stir-fry the pork strips and crushed garlic 3-4 minutes until browned.

Add the tomatoes, plum sauce and tomato ketchup and cook 3-4 minutes.

Meanwhile, in another non-stick pan or wok, place the boiled rice, red pepper, sweetcorn, spring onions, lemon juice and chilli sauce. Stir-fry 4-5 minutes until piping hot.

Serve half the pork and half the rice to each person.

Pork Satay

Serves 1

per serving   250   **10** 14

100g/3½ oz lean pork cubes
Salt and pepper
1 spring onions, finely sliced
1 level tbsp peanut butter
Pinch chilli powder
150ml/¼ pint chicken stock

Season pork cubes and grill until cooked through.

Place spring onions, peanut butter, chilli powder and chicken stock into a small saucepan. Heat through gently, stirring continuously, approximately 5 minutes or until ingredients are well blended and sauce thickens.

Stir pork cubes into sauce.

Serving suggestion

Boil 45g/1½ oz rice and serve with satay, accompanied by "free" salad or "free" vegetables stir-fried in spray oil.

per serving   400   **16** 15

or 1 Main Meal

Sticky Pork

Serves 1

per serving   250   **10** 7

| 175g/6 oz trimmed, lean pork steak |
| 1 dspn brown sugar |
| 1 dspn balsamic vinegar |
| 1 tsp light soy sauce |
| Pinch ground ginger |
| Spray oil |

Cut pork steak into 1 cm/½ inch strips. Mix together the sugar, balsamic vinegar, soy sauce and ginger. Coat pork strips in mixture.

Spray pan with oil and heat. Stir-fry the pork strips a few minutes until cooked through. Add remaining marinade to pan and cook until reduced to a sticky glaze.

Serving suggestion

Boil 45g/1½ oz rice or Chinese egg noodles and serve with Sticky Pork accompanied with "free" vegetables stir-fried in spray oil.

per serving   400   **16** 8

or 1 Main Meal

Pork & Pineapple Stir-fry

Serves 1

per serving   190

| 175g/6 oz lean pork mince |
| 1 clove garlic, crushed |
| 4-5 spring onions, trimmed and sliced |
| 2 rings pineapple in juice, drained and chopped |
| 1 dspn dark soy sauce |
| 1 tbsp dry sherry |
| 1 tsp sugar |
| 1 tbsp chopped coriander or parsley (optional) |

Place mince and garlic in a pan or wok and stir-fry 2-3 minutes to brown. Turn down heat, cover and cook gently 5 minutes. Drain any surplus fat.

Turn up heat and add spring onions, chopped pineapple, soy sauce, sherry and sugar. Stir-fry 2 minutes. Serve garnished with chopped coriander or parsley (optional).

Serving suggestion

Boil 85g/3 oz rice. Add 5 rounded tbsp frozen peas for last 5 minutes. Serve each person with half the rice and peas accompanied by half the Pork & Pineapple Stir-fry. You could also have "free" vegetables stir-fried in spray oil.

per serving   390   **16** 10

or 1 Main Meal

Beef & Mushroom in Oyster Sauce

Serves 1

per serving 150 6 4

100g/3½ oz lean rump or frying steak
Spray oil
4 mushrooms, preferably brown chestnut, cut into chunks
4-5 small florets broccoli
3 spring onions, sliced
3 tbsp oyster sauce (e.g. Sharwood's Real Oyster Sauce)

Cut steak across the grain into narrow strips. Spray pan with oil and heat. Add the steak strips and stir-fry 2-3 minutes.

Add the mushrooms, broccoli and spring onions and stir-fry a further 2-3 minutes. Add oyster sauce and heat through.

Serving suggestion

Boil 45g/1½ oz Chinese noodles and serve with the Beef & Mushroom.

per serving 300 **12** 5

or 1 Quick Meal

Boil 60g/2 oz Chinese noodles or rice and serve with the Beef & Mushroom.

per serving 350 **14** 5

or 1 Booster Main Meal.

Indonesian Dry Beef Curry

Serves 2

per serving   260   **10** 16

1 small onion, chopped
1 clove garlic, crushed
1 tbsp fresh chopped ginger
½ tsp chilli powder
½ tsp ground coriander
½ tsp turmeric
Good pinch of salt
3 tbsp water
200ml/⅓ pint reduced-fat canned coconut milk
225g/8 oz trimmed, lean braising steak
Lemon juice

Put the onion, garlic, ginger, chilli, coriander, turmeric, salt and water into a blender or food processor and blitz for a few seconds. Add the coconut milk and blitz until smooth.

Cut the steak into cubes and place in a saucepan together with the coconut milk mixture (ensure you shake can well before opening). Simmer gently, uncovered, 2 hours, or until meat is tender and sauce has become a thick, creamy paste. Stir frequently during cooking, and if it becomes too dry before the meat is tender, stir in 1-2 tbsp water. Squeeze in a little lemon juice and salt to taste, if necessary.

Serving suggestion

Boil 85g/3 oz rice. Serve each person with half the rice, half the curry and "free" vegetables such as Vegetable Bhajia (see page 41).

per serving   410   **16** 17

or 1 Main Meal

Keema One Pot Curry

Serves 1

per serving   390   **16** (16)

or 1 Main Meal

100g/3½ oz lean beef or pork mince
1 shallot or small onion, chopped
1 level dspn curry paste
300g can new potatoes, drained or 175g/6 oz cooked new potatoes
150ml/¼ pint hot water
1 dspn tomato purée
½ beef or chicken Oxo cube
2 rounded tbsp frozen peas
85g/3 oz cauliflower or broccoli florets, roughly chopped

Brown mince and shallot or onion in a saucepan. Cover and cook gently 5 minutes, stirring occasionally. Drain any surplus fat. Stir in curry paste and cook 1 minute.

Roughly chop the potatoes and add to the pan together with the water, tomato purée, crumbled stock cube, peas and cauliflower or broccoli. Mix together, cover and simmer gently 15 minutes, stirring occasionally.

Beef Madras

Serves 1

per serving   160   **6** 6

225g/8 oz trimmed, lean braising steak
Spray oil
1 onion, sliced
1-2 green chillis, de-seeded and sliced
1 clove garlic, crushed
1 tbsp hot curry powder
¼ tsp cinnamon
2 fresh or canned tomatoes, chopped
1 tbsp tomato puree
¼ tsp salt
275ml/½ pint hot water

Cut steak into cubes. Spray a saucepan with oil and heat. Brown meat on all sides. Remove meat from pan.

Add onions and green chilli to pan and cook until softened and starting to colour. Add a little water if necessary to prevent sticking. Add garlic, curry powder and cinnamon and stir-fry 1-2 minutes, until you can smell the aroma. (If using 2 chillis is still not hot enough for you, add some chilli powder also.)

Stir in the remaining ingredients, bring to a simmer, cover and cook very gently 2 hours, or until meat is very tender and sauce has reduced. Stir now and again and add a little extra water if it starts to dry out.

Serving suggestion

Boil 115g/4 oz basmati rice with ½ tsp turmeric, 2 cardamom pods, 2 cloves and salt to taste. Serve each person with half the rice and half the curry accompanied by cooling yoghurt Raita (see page 13) and "free" salad or vegetables.

per serving (including ½ quantity Raita)   405   **16** 8

or 1 Main Meal

Chicken Korma

Serves 2

per serving 260 **10** 12

85g/3 oz onion, sliced
Spray oil
150ml/¼ pint half-fat evaporated milk (e.g. Carnation Light)
1 tbsp korma curry paste (e.g. Patak's)
2 small skinless chicken breasts
1-2 tbsp skimmed milk (optional)
1 level tbsp dessicated coconut
Salt
2 tsp flaked almonds, lightly toasted
1 tsp finely chopped fresh coriander (optional)

Cook onions in a frying pan sprayed with oil until soft and golden. Add a little water if necessary to prevent sticking. Transfer to a blender or food processor together with the evaporated milk and curry paste. Blitz until smooth. Transfer to a small saucepan.

Cut chicken breasts into cubes. Re-spray frying pan and heat. Add chicken and cook 5-10 minutes, or until cooked through, stirring frequently.

Meanwhile, heat the sauce over moderate heat 3-5 minutes, stirring continuously. If it becomes too thick, stir in 1-2 tbsp skimmed milk . Stir in dessicated coconut and season to taste.

Stir cooked chicken into sauce and serve sprinkled with toasted flaked almonds.

Serving suggestion

Boil 85g/3 oz basmati rice. Serve each person with half the rice and half the Chicken Korma accompanied by "free" vegetables such as "free" Vegetable Bhajia (see page 41).

per serving 410 **16** 13

or 1 Main Meal

Quick Chicken Tikka Masala

Serves 1

per serving   190   **8** **5**

1 small onion, sliced
Spray oil
1 skinless chicken breasts, cubed
1 tsp tikka masala, or other, curry paste (e.g. Patak's)
200g small can/half of standard can tomatoes, chopped
1 rounded tbsp fat-free natural fromage frais
Garam masala (optional)

Soften onion in saucepan sprayed with oil, adding a little water if necessary to prevent sticking.

Add chicken cubes and stir-fry 3-4 minutes, stirring frequently.

Stir in curry paste and cook 30-60 seconds. Add tomatoes, breaking them up. Simmer 10-15 minutes. Remove from heat and stir in fromage frais. Serve sprinkled with garam masala (optional).

Serving suggestion

Simmer chopped "free" vegetables in 200g/half of standard can tomatoes with 1-2 tsp curry powder, salt and pepper to taste. Add water as necessary. Boil 60g/2 oz basmati rice. Serve rice with the Chicken Tikka Masala and the "free" vegetables.

per serving   190   **8** **5**

Balti Sauce

Serves 1

free food

350g/12 oz onions, finely chopped
3 cloves garlic, peeled and chopped
2 tbsp finely chopped fresh ginger
2-4 green chilles, de-seeded and chopped
10 cloves
Seeds from 10 green cardomom pods
1 tbsp each, ground cinnamon, turmeric, ground coriander, paprika
1 dspn cumin
2 tsp each, ground fenugreek and mustard powder
400g can tomatoes, chopped
600ml/good 1 pint water
Pared rind from 1 lemon & 2 tbsp lemon juice

Put onions, garlic and ginger in a large pan and add a little water. Cook 5 minutes stirring continuously until softened. Add chillies and cook 2 minutes. Add all the spices and stir on high heat 30 seconds. Stir in tomatoes, water, lemon rind, and lemon juice. Simmer, uncovered, 30 minutes. Discard lemon rind. Sauce is ready for use with freshly cooked or leftover poultry, prawns, vegetables etc. (see below). May be cooled and kept in the fridge several days.

Serving suggestions

Put one-quarter of the recipe into a saucepan. Add one of the following and heat through thoroughly:

60g/2 oz cooked weight chicken breast meat   90   **4** 1

60g/2 oz frozen cooked prawns, defrosted
Heat sauce first, add prawns and cook 1 minute   60   **2.5** 1

Cooked "free" vegetables   free food

See Check List, page 6, for additional items such as rice, naan breads, poppadums, etc.

Chicken Jalfrezi

Serves 4

per serving   190   **8** (10)

1 tbsp oil
2 onions, sliced
1 tbsp cumin seeds
1 tsp fresh grated ginger
2 cloves garlic, crushed
450g/1 lb skinless chicken breasts, cubed
3 different coloured peppers, de-seeded and sliced
2 tbsp tomato purée
2 tbsp medium or hot curry paste
Salt and pepper
Squeeze of lemon juice (optional)

Heat the oil in a frying pan and cook onions and cumin seeds until softened. Stir in ginger and garlic and cook 5 minutes.

Add the chicken and cook 10 minutes, stirring frequently. Stir in the tomato purée and curry paste. Add the sliced peppers, cover and cook approximately 10 minutes. Season with salt and pepper and lemon juice, if using.

Serving suggestion

Boil 225g/8 oz basmati rice. Serve each person with one-quarter of the rice and one-quarter of the Chicken Jalfrezi.

per serving   390   **16** (11)

Peking-style Duck with Noodles

Serves 1

per serving   500 **20** 9

or 1 Main Meal plus 4 Checks

2 cloves garlic, crushed
2.5cm/ 1 inch fresh ginger, finely chopped
1 tbsp soy sauce
1 tbsp honey
1 tbsp rice wine vinegar or white wine vinegar
1 tbsp sherry
2 tsp salt
675g/1½ lb duck breasts (including bone, skin and fat)
1 small cucumber
1 bunch spring onions
250g packet Chinese noodles
200g/7 oz plum sauce (e.g. Sharwood's)

Make a marinade from the garlic, ginger, soy sauce, honey, wine vinegar, sherry and salt. Remove the skin, fat and bone from the duck breasts and place in a shallow dish. Pour over the marinade, cover and refrigerate 4 hours.

Pre-heat oven to 190°C/gas mark 5 and roast the duck breasts on a rack 30 minutes. Reserve the marinade.

Cut cucumber and spring onions into long thin strips. Remove duck breasts from oven and slice. Boil the noodles and drain. Heat marinade to boiling point and stir in the plum sauce.

Serve each person with one-quarter of the noodles, vegetables and duck with sauce poured over.

Thai-style Red Chicken Curry

Serves 2

per serving   290   **12** 14

| 2 dspn Thai red curry paste |
| 200ml/½ can reduced-fat coconut milk |
| 2 skinless chicken breasts |
| 2 dspn Thai fish sauce or light soy sauce |
| 2 tsp sugar |
| 1 small aubergine, cut into cubes |
| 2 dspn lime or lemon juice |

Mix curry paste with coconut milk. Boil uncovered to reduce by one-third.

Cut chicken breasts into 6-8 pieces each and add to coconut milk and curry paste. Cover and simmer gently 5 minutes, stirring occasionally.

Add fish sauce or soy sauce, sugar and aubergine cubes to chicken. Simmer gently a further 10 minutes, stirring occasionally. Stir in lime or lemon juice before serving.

Serving suggestion

Boil 60g/2 oz rice. Serve half the rice to each person together with half the curry.

per serving   390   **16** 15

or 1 Main Meal

Boil 115g/4 oz rice. Serve half the rice to each person together with half the curry.

per serving   490   **20** 15

or 1 Main Meal plus 4 Checks

Asian & Oriental
Chicken in Blackbean Sauce

Serves 1

per serving 200 **8** 3

3 spring onions
3-4 mushrooms
1 small carrot
1 skinless chicken breast
Spray oil
3 tbsp black bean sauce (e.g. Sharwood's)

Slice spring onions and mushrooms. Peel and cut carrot into small, thin strips, or chop finely. Cut chicken in 6-8 cubes.

Spray pan with oil and heat. Stir-fry the chicken 3 minutes.

Add spring onions, mushrooms and carrots to the pan and stir-fry until carrots are just tender, about 2-3 minutes. Turn down heat, stir in the black bean sauce and warm through.

Serving suggestion

Boil 60g/2 oz Chinese egg noodles and serve with the Chicken in Black bean sauce.

per serving 400 **16** 4

or 1 Main Meal

Sweet & Sour Chicken

Serves 4

per serving 175

2 tbsp light soy sauce
2 tbsp dry sherry
1 tsp Chinese 5-spice powder
350g/12 oz skinless chicken breast, cubed
1 tbsp cornflour
2 tbsp white vinegar
1 tbsp sugar
1 tbsp tomato purée
1 chicken stock cube (e.g. Knorr)
150ml/¼ pint hot water
227g can pineapple pieces in juice
Spray oil
1 onion, sliced
1 carrot, finely sliced or cut into thin strips
1 red or green pepper, de-seeded and sliced
225g/8 oz beansprouts

Mix together 1 tbsp light soy sauce, sherry and 5-spice powder. Marinate the chicken cubes in this mixture at least 1 hour.

Mix cornflour with vinegar, sugar and tomato purée. Dissolve stock cube in hot water and add pineapple juice from can. Mix the stock and juice with the cornflour mixture. Spray a pan or wok with oil and heat. Add the chicken, onion, carrots and peppers and stir-fry approximately 10 minutes until chicken is cooked through. Stir in beansprouts and pineapple pieces. Stir in cornflour and stock mixture, and remaining marinade. Bring to the boil, stirring, and cook 1-2 minutes until thickened.

Serving suggestion

Boil 250g pack Sharwood's fine or medium egg noodles. Serve each person with one-quarter of the noodles and one-quarter of the Sweet & Sour Chicken.

per serving 375

Takeaway Lemon Chicken

Serves 1

per serving   220   **9**   2

4 skinless chicken breasts
85g/3 oz wholemeal breadcrumbs
Salt and pepper
Spray oil
A little skimmed milk
1 tsp cornflour
Grated zest of half a lemon
3 tbsp lemon juice
1 tbsp sugar
150ml/¼ pint water
Granulated sweetener (optional)

Pre-heat oven to 190°C/gas mark 5.

Slice chicken breasts horizontally across to make 3 slices each. Season the breadcrumbs. Spray a non-stick baking tray with oil and spread crumbs over tray. Dip chicken breasts in skimmed milk then lay them on the crumbs. Use surrounding crumbs to cover the top of the chicken pieces. Spray lightly with oil and bake 25-30 minutes, turning halfway through.

Put cornflour into a saucepan and stir in lemon zest and juice. Add sugar and water and bring to the boil, stirring continuously until sauce thickens. If sauce is too sharp for your taste, stir in 1-2 tsp granulated sweetener.

Serving suggestion

Boil 175g/6 oz rice with a chicken stock cube and chopped "free" vegetables. Serve each person with one-quarter of the chicken and sauce accompanied by one-quarter of the rice and vegetable mixture.

per serving   370   **15**   3

Vegetable Bhajia

Serves 1

free food

2 medium onions, sliced
1 clove garlic, chopped
2 dspn curry powder
1 tsp turmeric
1 Oxo vegetable cube
400ml/⅔ pint hot water
1 tbsp tomato purée
1 tbsp lemon juice
450g/1 lb cauliflower florets
2 medium carrots, sliced
250g/9 oz frozen sliced green beans
1-2 tomatoes, chopped
Salt

Spread sliced onions and garlic over base of a large non-stick saucepan (or spray an ordinary saucepan lightly with oil). Cover and cook over low heat 15 minutes until soft and starting to brown. Sprinkle in curry powder and turmeric. Cover and cook over very low heat 2-3 minutes to release spice flavours.

Dissolve stock cube in hot water and stir into pan together with tomato purée, lemon juice, cauliflower and carrots. Cover and simmer gently 30-45 minutes, stirring occasionally.

Add green beans and tomatoes, cover and simmer 10-15 minutes. Season to taste.

Serve as an accompaniment to curries.

Serving suggestion

Serve a portion of the Vegetable Bhajia with 1 mini naan and 1 dspn mango chutney.

per serving 230   9 7

or 1 Booster Quick Meal

Vegetable Biryani

Serves 1

per serving   410   **16** (14)

or 1 Main Meal

1 medium egg, hard-boiled
275ml/½ pint water
225g/8 oz mixture "free" vegetables, (e.g. cauliflower, broccoli, green beans, carrots)
1 tbsp korma curry paste (e.g. Patak's)
1 tbsp tomato purée
1 tsp turmeric
75g/2½ oz rice
1-2 fresh or canned tomatoes, roughly chopped
Salt
Garam masala (optional)

Bring the water to the boil and add the "free" vegetables. Cover and cook 10 minutes.

Stir in the curry paste, tomato purée, turmeric and rice. Cover and cook gently 15-20 minutes.

Remove lid, add the tomatoes and cook gently 2-3 minutes, until any excess moisture is absorbed. Season to taste.

Shell the egg and slice. Serve the biryani garnished with the egg slices and sprinkled with a little garam masala (optional).

Spiced Cauliflower, Potato & Spinach

Serves 2

per serving   230   **9** 9

or 1 Booster Quick Meal

400g/14 oz potatoes, peeled
1 onion, sliced
Spray oil
2 tbsp curry paste, mild or hot
275ml/½ pint hot water
Salt
200g/7 oz small cauliflower florets
150g/5 oz frozen spinach
2 large fresh or canned tomatoes, roughly chopped

Cut the potatoes into large chunky pieces.

Brown the onions in a large saucepan sprayed with oil. Add curry paste and potatoes and cook 1 minute, stirring. Add hot water, salt lightly and bring to the boil, then cover and simmer 15 minutes.

Add cauliflower, spinach and tomatoes. Cover 5-10 minutes until spinach has defrosted, stirring now and again. Simmer, uncovered, 10-15 minutes until cauliflower is to your liking. Season to taste.

Serving suggestion

Add 4 rounded tbsp canned chickpeas or blackeye beans when adding the spinach and tomatoes. If required, add extra water during final simmering. Serve half the recipe to each person.

per serving   290   **12** 10

or 1 Quick Meal
or 1 Booster Main Meal

Easy Dahl

Serves 3

per serving   150   **6** 9

1 small onion, chopped
Spray oil
425g can pease pudding
1 can full of water
2 tbsp korma curry paste (e.g. Patak's)

Soften the onion in a medium saucepan sprayed with oil.

Add the pease pudding and break up with a fork. Gradually stir in the water, about one-third at a time, mixing well. Stir in the curry paste.

Cook very gently, as the dahl may splash. Stir for 2-3 minutes to heat through and add a little more water if it becomes too thick.

Serving suggestion

Boil 200g/7 oz rice. Serve each person with one-third of the rice and one-third of the dahl, accompanied by "free" vegetables or "free" Vegetable Bhajia (see page 41)

per serving   380   **15** 10

Egg Fu Yung

Serves 1

per serving   170

2 eggs
1 tsp light soy sauce
1 tsp dry sherry (optional)
Spray oil
2 spring onions, trimmed and sliced
60g/2 oz sliced red or green pepper
60g/2 oz beansprouts

Beat the 2 eggs and stir in soy sauce and dry sherry, if using.

Spray pan with oil and heat. Stir fry spring onions and peppers 2 minutes. Add beansprouts and stir-fry 30 seconds.

Turn down heat and tip beaten eggs over the vegetables in the pan. As the edges cook, draw them towards the centre and allow uncooked egg to spill out to the edges to cook. Cook until egg is just set. Transfer to a serving dish and sprinkle with a few more drops of light soy sauce, if liked.

Serving suggestion

Boil 30g/1 oz Chinese noodles and serve with Egg Fu Yung.

per serving   270

or 1 Quick Meal

Marinated Tofu Stir-fry

Serves 2

per serving   375   **15** (15)

or 1 Main Meal

115g/4 oz rice
175g/6 oz firm tofu
1 tbsp light soy sauce
1 tbsp cornflour
2 dspn oil
85g/3 oz mushrooms, sliced
1 red pepper, de-seeded and sliced
115g/4 oz small broccoli florets
Salt and pepper

Boil rice and set aside.

Cut the tofu into 1 cm/½ inch cubes and marinate in the soy sauce 30 minutes. Reserve the marinade and toss the tofu in the cornflour.

Heat the oil in a frying pan or wok and stir-fry the tofu cubes 4-5 minutes until golden. Remove tofu and keep warm.

Add the mushrooms, peppers and broccoli to the pan and stir-fry 3-4 minutes. Add the boiled rice and reserved marinade and heat through. Season to taste and serve with the tofu.

Vegetable or Prawn Spring Rolls

Makes 6 rolls

per roll   170   **7**   1

Spray oil
1 small onion, finely chopped
1 carrot, peeled and coarsely grated
200g/7 oz beansprouts
100g/3½ oz canned sweetcorn or cooked prawns
1 tbsp light soy sauce
1 tbsp dry sherry
1 tsp Chinese 5-spice powder
Pinch of ground ginger
6 x 45g sheets filo pastry (e.g. Jus-rol)

Stir-fry onion in pan sprayed with oil until softened. Add carrots and beansprouts.

Mix together soy sauce, sherry, 5-spice powder and ginger and add to pan. Stir-fry 2 minutes then stir in sweetcorn or cooked prawns. Set aside and allow to cool.

Pre-heat oven to 190°C/gas mark 5.

Take 1 sheet of filo and cover remaining sheets with clingfilm until you use them, to prevent drying out. Spay one side of the sheet lightly with oil and fold over in half. Put one-sixth of the vegetable mixture at one end, roll up tucking in ends and place on a baking tray. Repeat with remaining filo sheets.

Spray the rolls with oil and bake approximately 10-15 minutes or until golden.

Serving suggestion

Serve 2 rolls with "free" salad

per serving   340   **14**   2

or 1 Quick Meal plus 2 Checks

Quorn Green Curry

Serves 4

per serving   225   **9** 18

2 dspn oil
350g pack Quorn pieces
1 clove garlic, crushed
400ml can reduced-fat coconut milk
1 tbsp Thai green curry paste
1 tbsp light soy sauce
1 tsp sugar
15 fresh basil leaves

Heat the oil in a wok or large pan. Add the Quorn and garlic and stir-fry 3-4 minutes until golden.

Add the coconut milk, curry paste, soy sauce and sugar. Stir and simmer gently 5 minutes.

Add the basil leaves and simmer 2 minutes more.

Serving suggestion

Boil 200g/7oz rice. Serve each person with one-quarter of the rice and one quater of the curry accompanied by steamed broccoli and green beans or other "free" vegetables.

per serving   400   **16** 19

or 1 Main Meal